Fit for the E

A Guide to Care of the Horse's Mouth

First published in 2010 by
The Pony Club
Stoneleigh Park
Kenilworth
Warwickshire
CV8 2RW

Publishing Consultant: Barbara Cooper
Design and Production: Paul Harding
Distribution: Quiller Publishing Ltd.

ISBN 978-1-907279-08-9

2 4 5 3 1

British Library Cataloguing in Publication Data available on request.

Printed in China

STABLEMATES

Fit for the Bit

A Guide to Care of the Horse's Mouth

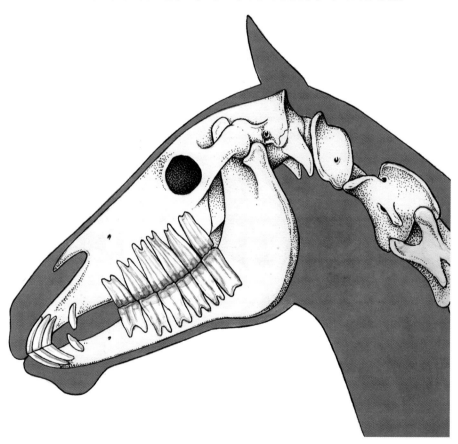

Antony de Csernatony

Maggie Raynor

Contents

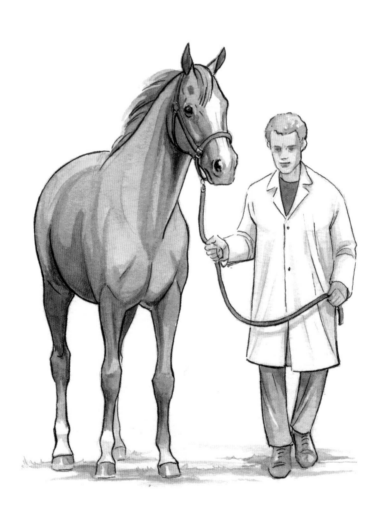

Introduction

We humans generally have our teeth checked by a dentist every six months. We all know how painful a problem within the mouth can be: an abscess, a lost filling, gum disease. Nothing life-threatening, but enough to cause a great deal of pain and discomfort if left unattended. Taking this into consideration it is therefore surprising to discover how little thought many of us give to our horses' teeth. Perhaps at some point we have felt that Equine Dental Technicians (EDTs) are only deemed necessary among the full-time professionals in our sport: i.e. for the true performance horse. After all, horses have survived in the wild for thousands of years without fillings or the need for a quick polish!

Recent studies amongst veterinarians and EDTs have shown that compared with the population of horses living in the wild, almost three quarters of the domestic horse population suffers significant dental problems. By domesticating horses we have changed their diet and grazing habits; we have affected what they eat and how they eat, and in so doing we have altered the natural wear-pattern of their teeth. Many of the problems suffered by so many horses of all breeds and ages can be directly linked to poor or non-existent dental maintenance. It is certainly not by deliberate intention that we ignore this aspect of the horse's welfare but is perhaps through a lack of understanding of the vitally important part played by a healthy mouth and teeth in a horse's physical and mental wellbeing.

At some point in our lives with horses, whether as casual weekend riders or as full-time professionals, we have all experienced or heard about horses who buck, rear, nap, bolt, headshake, or just fail to gain condition despite our best efforts. These could be problems brought on not by the horse being naughty or ill-tempered, but possibly by the lack of good oral and dental care. To begin to work towards that elusive harmonious balance between horse and rider we must first understand the important part played by the horse's mouth and teeth in his overall wellbeing. Remember that good oral and dental health equals good condition and performance. To have a successful and rewarding relationship with our horse we must first have a happy horse. I hope that this book will help you to achieve that aim.

K de Cserhey   M. Raynor

The Origins of the Horse

The first true horse species (*equids*), known as *Hyracotherium* or *Eohippus* ('dawn horse') evolved approximately 54 million years ago—some 10 million years after the dinosaur. They had four toes on their front feet and three on the back, and they bore little resemblance to present-day horses, being more dog-like in appearance. These early equine ancestors were forest dwellers, whose diet consisted of soft tropical fruits and protein-rich plants. They had low or short-crowned teeth, ideal for browsing in the tropical forests.

In time the lush forests began to shrink in size, giving way to open plains covered with drier and much coarser plants, and as the vegetation and climate change so did the equids, whose legs lengthened and hooves developed. With their longer legs these grass-eaters were able to run swiftly, which was necessary on the open plains. In turn their necks lengthened, enabling them to graze on the shorter grass, which was much tougher than the plants in the tropical forests. Their teeth thus had to evolve to cope with their new, more abrasive diet, the short-crowned teeth of the early horse being replaced by ones whose main function was to grind. The teeth also became tougher, with small crests connected together to form ridges for grinding. The height of the tooth-crowns also grew, so that as the teeth wore down they could erupt out of the gum when necessary.

To sum up, these newly-evolved horses had long necks, long legs and deep jaws. Their teeth were high-crowned, with the elongation of the face and the deepening of the jaw allowing the space needed for the constantly erupting teeth. The strong crests were now lined with cement to cope with the constant grinding and wearing down. This in turn resulted in a much longer lifespan. *Equus Caballus*, the true horse, had arrived.

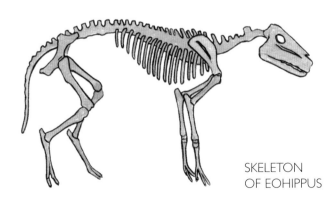

SKELETON
OF EOHIPPUS

EVOLUTION OF THE HORSE

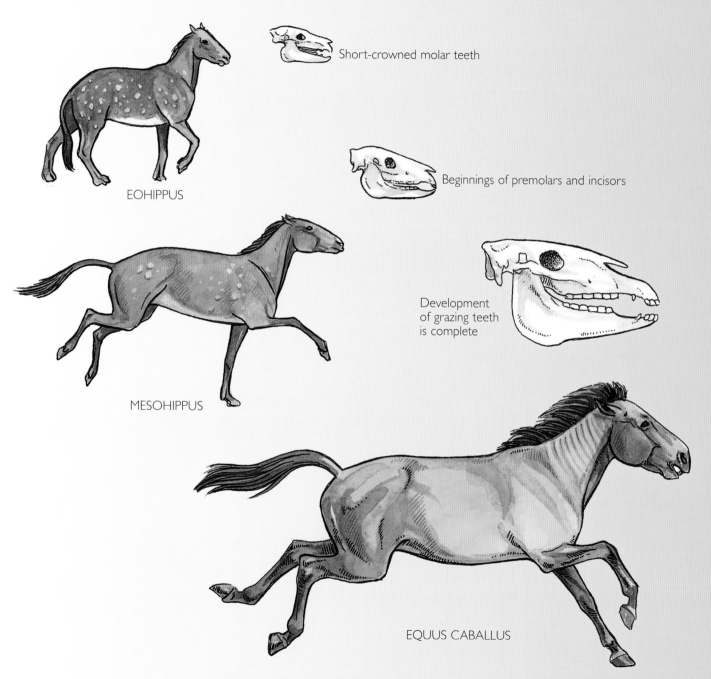

Short-crowned molar teeth

EOHIPPUS

Beginnings of premolars and incisors

Development of grazing teeth is complete

MESOHIPPUS

EQUUS CABALLUS

A Brief History

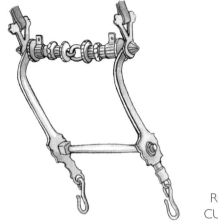

ROMAN
CURB BIT

It is commonly believed that the serious study of horses' teeth dates back no more than about a century, whereas interest in the subject was actually first shown as early as 600 BC by the Chinese, who discovered that a horse's teeth could be used to determine his age. The Greeks and Romans also made advancements in the field: for example, diseases of the horse's mouth were written about by Aristotle in his *History of Animals* (333 BC). Much later, Leonardo da Vinci showed interest in the subject, but it then seems to have been abandoned for several centuries.

As horses began to be used for transportation, agricultural and military purposes, the importance of care of their teeth became apparent to their owners. Healthy mouths and teeth would result in good performance and longevity, greatly enhancing the horse's value. It is now thought that owners taught themselves how to alter the shape and characteristics of their horses' teeth so that the animals would appear younger and therefore be more valuable.

The science of equine dentistry was actually first recognised around 1207 AD, but another 500 years were to pass before the first veterinary college in the western world was set up in France in 1762. Yet another century passed by before the next college was opened in the USA in 1862. There are various old paintings in existence depicting horses having their teeth rasped, as well as hand-made dental instruments forged by blacksmiths in the 1600s. The first English company making instruments for equine dentistry was Arnold & Sons in 1817. The first books on the subject were published in 1889.

As horses were less and less used in the workplace and gradually replaced by machinery, they began to take on new roles in sport and recreation. There was therefore less emphasis on oral care, and no further advancement in the field of equine dentistry took place until the 1980s, when the first school dedicated purely to the subject opened its doors in the USA. One of its founders was Dale Jeffery, who also went on to write several important specialist books.

In 2001, Hartpury College became the first educational centre in the UK to offer students the opportunity to obtain a Batchelor of Science degree in Equine Dentistry.

Why Do Horses' Teeth Need to be Looked After?

It is important to understand that unlike human teeth those of the horse erupt continuously from the gum throughout their life. They grow approximately 2 to 3 millimetres a year, and should be worn away by chewing at the same rate. However, when we domesticate animals we interfere with nature's way, and 'survival of the fittest' no longer applies; we have taken the horse away from his natural environment, changed his diet, and created a routine which suits our own lifestyle rather than that of the animal. Although there are many areas throughout the world where herds of horses live in an environment unaffected by man—such as Exmoor, the New Forest and mustang country in the USA—these places are untamed rather than wild. The only remaining truly wild horse in the world, although sadly on the verge of extinction, is the Przewalski.

The most significant change that we have brought about in the horse is to his diet and natural grazing habits. A wild horse will travel many miles each day in the search for food. His diet will consist of coarse grasses, plants and shrubs with thorny stems and even twigs and small branches from young trees. The horse's digestive system was designed for the 'little and often' style of grazing, and when we remove him from this environment we immediately start to create problems. While the wild horse will spend anything up to 20 hours a day grazing, the domesticated horse often spends the same amount of time confined to a stable or paddock. The hard, abrasive diet of the wild horse has been replaced by soft hay and lush pasture grass. The use of haynets and mangers changes the natural grazing position of the horse, creating uneven wear of the teeth.

'Survival of the fittest' is nature's way of ensuring that only the strongest and healthiest will survive: in the wild, horses with any physical weakness tend not to have a long life-expectancy. A horse with bad teeth or poor dentition would not survive long enough to pass on any hereditary problems. The domesticated horse is bred for traits such as conformation, jumping ability, speed and endurance, with no regard for dentition. In creating miniature breeds and horses for the show-ring with fine, pretty heads, we have created significant dental problems. In short, domestication is one of the main reasons why our horses now require regular dental maintenance.

The Head and How the Mouth Works

A horse's head is made up of 34 bones, which are mostly flat and overlap one another to assist during the birthing process. The bones of the forehead and cheeks are dense, forming a protective barrier around the brain. The frontal and nasal bones create the sinus and nasal cavity. The last three molars of the upper jaw jut into the sinus cavity.

The jawbone is the foundation of the tooth. The upper jawbone is part of the skull and is wider than the lower jaw. The lower jaw is attached to the skull by the jaw or *temporomandibular* joint. This is situated just behind the eye and allows the horse to open his mouth horizontally and move it from side to side. When the horse chews food, the lower jaw, being mobile, moves in a circular motion, grinding and crushing the food on the fixed upper jaw.

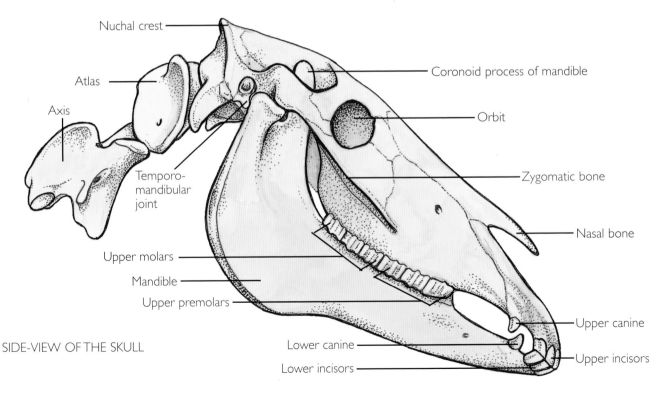

Nuchal crest

Atlas

Axis

Temporo-mandibular joint

Coronoid process of mandible

Orbit

Zygomatic bone

Nasal bone

Upper molars

Mandible

Upper premolars

Upper canine

Lower canine

Lower incisors

Upper incisors

SIDE-VIEW OF THE SKULL

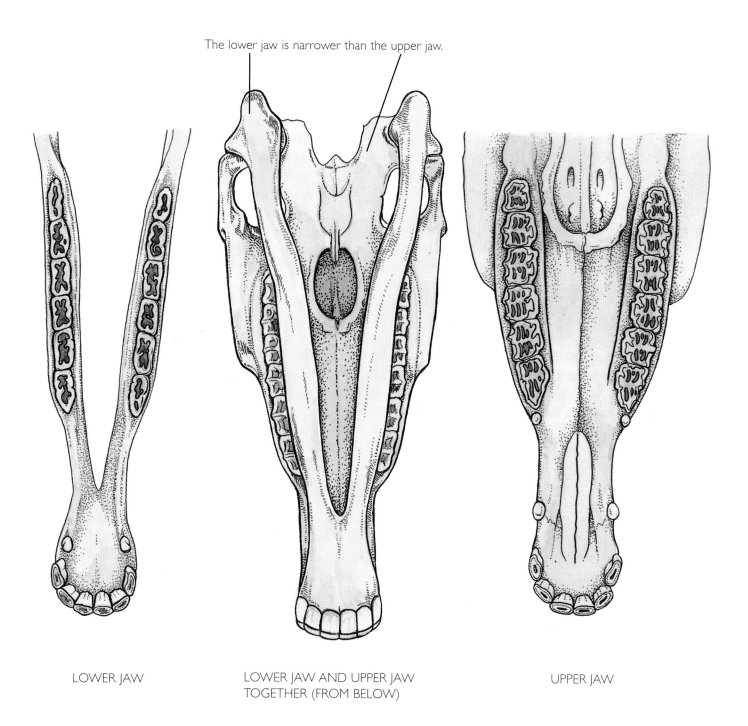

The lower jaw is narrower than the upper jaw.

LOWER JAW

LOWER JAW AND UPPER JAW
TOGETHER (FROM BELOW)

UPPER JAW

The muscles of the head enable the horse to feed, chew and digest his food. The lip muscles allow the horse to drink and take in food. The tongue muscles help to move the food back and towards the grinding molar teeth, which in turn are operated by the jaw bone and powerful cheek muscles.

The blood, containing oxygen which is essential for the health and efficiency of the muscles, is carried via a network of arteries and veins.

The nerves of the face branch out, enabling the reception of stimuli in the sensory organs and facilitating movement and control of the muscles.

There are three main salivary glands in the head: the *parotid*, *mandibular* and *sublingual*. Saliva plays a vital role in chewing and digestion, and helps to keep the whole mouth clean and lubricated.

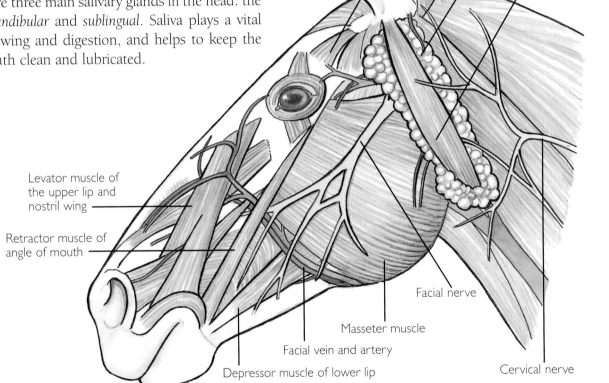

Temporalis muscle

Parotid salivary gland

Parotid auricular muscle

Levator muscle of the upper lip and nostril wing

Retractor muscle of angle of mouth

Facial nerve

Masseter muscle

Facial vein and artery

Depressor muscle of lower lip

Cervical nerve

SUBCUTANEOUS STRUCTURES OF THE HEAD

Chewing and Digestion

When a horse is grazing he carefully selects grass with his sensitive lips and then nips it off with his front incisor teeth. When there is a sufficient amount of grass in the mouth, the tongue pushes the food back towards the molars where it is crushed and ground into smaller particles. The upper jaw is fixed, whilst the lower jaw is moveable. The horse chews in a circular motion, the lower jaw grinding against the upper jaw. The hard palate or roof of the mouth has ridges which help to move the food back, but also prevent it from falling out of the mouth.

Once the chewing action has begun, it is important for the food to be ground as small as possible. Large particles are difficult for a horse to digest and can lead to balls of food obstructing the intestines, causing colic. Chewing is also important to ensure that the maximum nutritional value is obtained from the food. Uneven wear on the teeth can sometimes be caused by the horse using one side of his mouth more predominantly than the other for chewing

The sight of food causes saliva to be secreted in the mouth: an average horse can produce up to 10 gallons/ 45 litres a day. As the horse chews, saliva is secreted in great quantities, helping the horse to swallow and digest the food. Once it has been ground down it is moved to the gullet for the next stage of digestion.

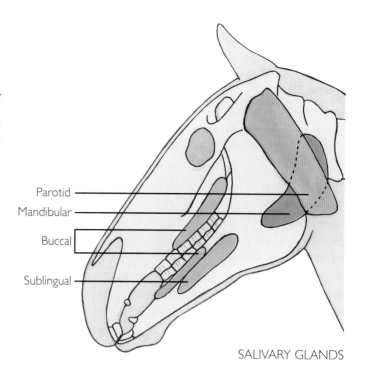

Parotid

Mandibular

Buccal

Sublingual

SALIVARY GLANDS

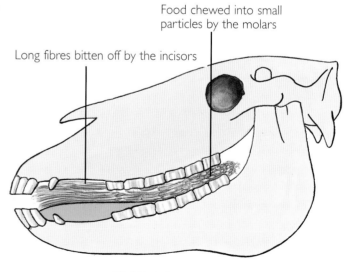

Food chewed into small particles by the molars

Long fibres bitten off by the incisors

FOOD MOVING THROUGH THE MOUTH

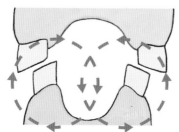

CIRCULAR CHEWING PATTERN
Only one circle will be used at a time

15

What is a Tooth Made of?

Horses' teeth are made up of three tissues: *dentine*, *enamel* and *cementum*. The main source of food for the horse is grass, which contains a large amount of silica. Their teeth, therefore, have to be strong and resilient enough to cope with this abrasive diet.

Dentine makes up the biggest part of the tooth. It is softer than enamel and although it decays more rapidly it has the ability to repair certain defects, and continues to form throughout the horse's life. Creamy yellow in colour, dentine has a degree of sensitivity to hot and cold.

Enamel is an inorganic material, which means that it has a very high proportion of minerals and a very small percentage of water. Although it is the hardest substance found in the body it is also extremely brittle and once destroyed cannot be repaired.

Cementum is the third building-block of the horse's tooth. Compared to enamel and dentine, cementum is soft, which enables it to be relatively flexible. The structure is similar to that of bone. As horses age, their teeth begin to darken or stain. This is caused by pigments from food being absorbed by the cementum, and bears no reflection on the health of the tooth.

The pulp is the central part of the tooth and is filled with soft connective tissue. This tissue, containing blood vessels and nerves, enters the pulp chamber through a hole in the tip of the root.

The major part of the tooth lies unseen below the gum line, embedded in the jawbone. This part of the tooth is known as the 'reserve crown'. The root lies below the reserve crown contained in the socket. The root anchors the tooth in the jaw bone . The part of the tooth above the gum line is called the 'visible crown'.

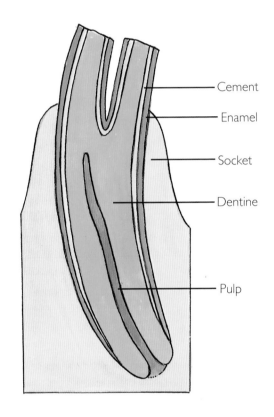

STRUCTURE OF AN INCISOR TOOTH

- Cement
- Enamel
- Socket
- Dentine
- Pulp

The length of a horse's molar tooth at approximately 7 years of age is 8cm; 1–1½ cm of this is the visible crown, with 7cm hidden below the gum line. The teeth wear away at approximately 2–3mm per year—which means that by 30 years of age there is very little reserve crown left, and eruption ceases to take place.

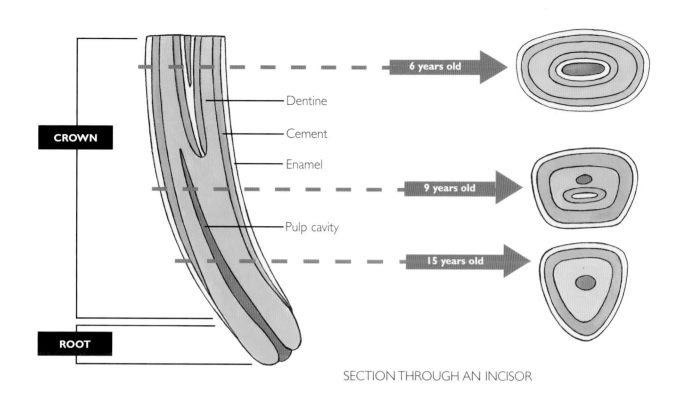

CROWN

ROOT

Dentine

Cement

Enamel

Pulp cavity

6 years old

9 years old

15 years old

SECTION THROUGH AN INCISOR

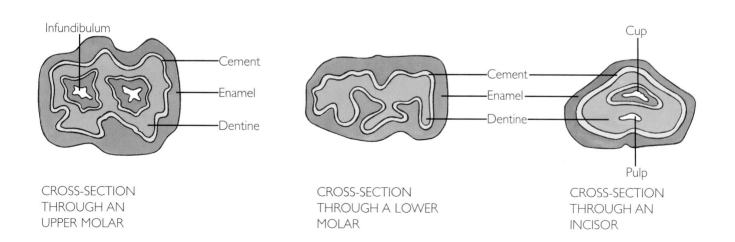

Infundibulum

Cement

Enamel

Dentine

CROSS-SECTION
THROUGH AN
UPPER MOLAR

Cement

Enamel

Dentine

CROSS-SECTION
THROUGH A LOWER
MOLAR

Cup

Cement

Enamel

Dentine

Pulp

CROSS-SECTION
THROUGH AN
INCISOR

Tooth Growth and Development

TEETH AT 2 YEARS OLD

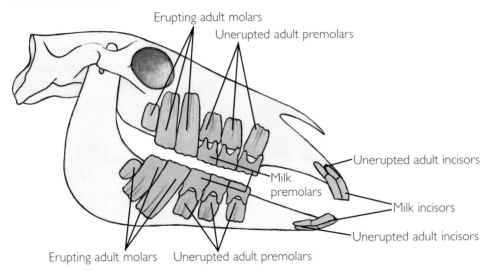

Erupting adult molars
Unerupted adult premolars
Unerupted adult incisors
Milk premolars
Milk incisors
Unerupted adult incisors
Erupting adult molars
Unerupted adult premolars

TEETH AT 6 YEARS OLD

TEETH AT 28 YEARS OLD

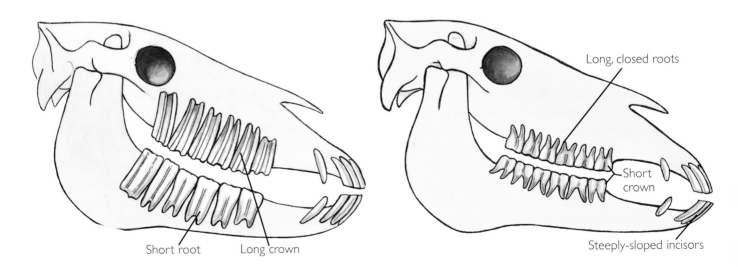

Short root
Long crown

Long, closed roots
Short crown
Steeply-sloped incisors

Tooth Growth

The tooth bud
lies in the jawbone.

The building blocks of the tooth
(dentine, enamel, and cement)
are formed whilst the tooth
continues to develop.

As the tooth develops it pushes against the gum,
which becomes swollen, finally erupting
into the mouth

Development continues until
the opposing teeth meet.

The opposing teeth now grind against
each other as the horse chews food.

A continuation of grind, wear
and eruption takes place.

By 25–30 years the major part of the
tooth is used and eruption ceases.

Tooth Eruption and Development

Birth
Deciduous (baby) premolars are present.

▼

6 to 8 days
2 central deciduous incisors upper and lower.

▼

6 to 8 weeks
2 lateral deciduous incisors, upper and lower.

▼

6 to 8 months
2 corner deciduous incisors, upper and lower.

▼

6 to 18 months
Wolf teeth appear.

▼

12 months
Full set of deciduous incisors, upper and lower.

▼

1 to 3 years
Permanant molars develop and erupt into the mouth.

▼

2 years 6 months
Central incisors pushed out by permanent teeth
and 1st permanent premolars erupt.

▼

3 years
Permanent central incisors fully developed.
Eruption of 2nd permanent premolars.

▼

3 years 6 months
Milk teeth lateral incisors, upper and lower, are replaced by
permanent teeth. Eruption of 3rd permanant premolars.

▼

4 years
Lateral permanent incisors are fully developed.

▼

4 years 6 months
Milk teeth corner incisors replaced by permanent teeth.

▼

4 to 5 years
Corner incisors are fully developed. Canines may appear.

▼

5 to 6 years
Full set of permanent teeth.

Ageing

Between birth and 5 years, a horse undergoes major changes in his mouth. Determining his age during this period is relatively accurate.

By the age of 5, a horse has a full set of permanent teeth. At 7 years a hook may appear on the upper corner incisors. This is caused through a change in the position of the lower incisors, resulting in a smaller part of the upper tooth coming into contact. However, the hook disappears and then reappears at about 11 years, and so ageing the horse on the hook alone cannot be relied on for accuracy.

From 6 years, age is determined by the shape of and the wear pattern on the teeth. As the teeth are ground down with age, the appearance of the chewing surface will alter. *Cups* are black cavities of varying depths filled with dentine. They are found on the chewing surface of the incisor teeth. Between 6 and 11 years of age the cups are gradually worn away—leaving only a small dot on the chewing surface. This is known as the *mark*.

The *dental star* is the tooth pulp sealed with dentine, indicated by a small light brown mark found in front of the cup.

With age, the upper and lower incisors begin to alter position. In a young horse, viewed from the side, the profile of the upper and lower teeth and gums is almost straight. With increasing age the angle becomes more acute and the teeth appear to protrude. However, as a horse grows older it becomes more difficult to

1 YEAR OLD
A 1-year-old horse has a full mouth of temporary incisors.

2 YEARS OLD
A full mouth of temporary incisors.
By the age of 2, all the temporary incisors are in wear: i.e. they are level with the adjacent teeth.

3 YEARS OLD
In the mouth of a 3-year-old horse the central temporary incisors (DI 1) have been shed and replaced by permanent incisors (PI 1).

4 YEARS OLD
Between the ages of 3 and 4 the lateral permanent incisors (PI 2) erupt and replace the temporary lateral incisors (DI 2); so the 4-year-old horse has four permanent incisors in wear.

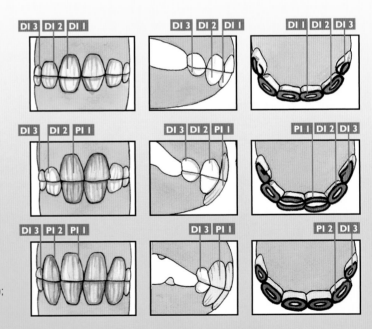

determine his age accurately, as outside factors such as diet, breed and possible vices—for example, crib biting—come into play.

In the early 1900s an Australian horseman called Sydney Galvayne set about devising a method by which the age of a horse could be determined. While working in Europe he quickly realized the benefit of correctly ageing horses by the appearance of their teeth. Owners also recognized the value of this: some even tried to alter their horse's teeth in an attempt to create a 'younger mouth'.

Galvayne's Groove can be found on the outer surface of the upper corner incisors on both sides of the upper jaw. It begins to reveal its bottom point at the gum line at approx 10 years of age. As the tooth is worn away and replaced, more of the groove is revealed. By the age of 20 it will extend all the way down the visible part of the tooth. By the age of 30 the whole length of the groove will have been worn away and none of it will remain in the rest of the hidden crown or in the root of the tooth.

Galvayne's Groove is not always present however, and even when it is, it can vary from one side of the mouth to the other. It is not particularly accurate and at best can be used to make an educated guess.

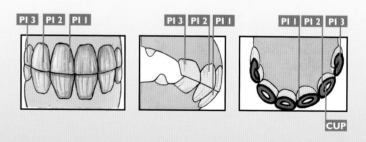

KEY		
	DI 1	central temporary incisor
	DI 2	lateral temporary incisor
	DI 3	corner temporary incisor
	PI 1	central permanent incisor
	PI 2	lateral permanent incisor
	PI 3	corner permanent incisor

5 YEARS OLD

At 5 years old the corner permanent incisors (PI 3) replace the temporary corner incisors (DI 3); the 5-year-old horse will have a full mouth of permanent teeth.

6 YEARS OLD

At 6 years all the incisors are in wear, and all show a central 'cup' (or infundibulum). The canine teeth will be present, as they erupt between the ages of 4 and 5.

7 YEARS OLD

A hook develops at the rear of the upper corner incisor which disappears at the age of 8. At 7 years the 'cup' in the central incisors has disappeared, but the 'mark' (an outer ring of enamel filled with cement) will be visible..

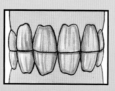

8 YEARS OLD

At 8 years the 'cup' has gone from the lateral incisors, but the 'mark' is still visible. The 'dental star' (secondary dentine exposed in the pulp cavity) can be seen on the central incisors.

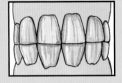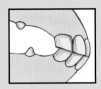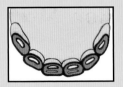

9 YEARS OLD

At 9 years the 'cups' have gone from all the incisors, but the 'marks' are still present. 'The dental star' is now seen on the lateral incisors, and another hook has formed on the upper corner incisors. The central incisors have become triangular in shape. Galvayne's groove (a dark coloured groove appearing on the upper corner incisors) begins to be visible between the ages of 9 and 10.

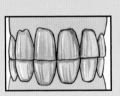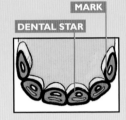

10 YEARS OLD

At 10 years the 'marks' are less pronounced, but the 'dental stars' are more distinct. Galvayne's groove has grown longer. The lateral incisors have become triangular in shape, and all the incisors have begun to slope forwards.

12 YEARS OLD

At 12 years the 'mark' has gone from the central incisors, but the 'star' is still visible. The 'stars' are now round and distinct. The shape of all the incisors is triangular.

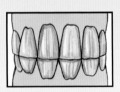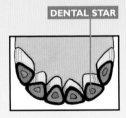

15 YEARS OLD

At 15 years the 'marks' have gone from every incisor, replaced by a centrally situated 'dental star'. Galvayne's groove extends half-way down the tooth. The angle of the incisors has become noticeably more sloping.

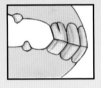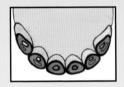

19 YEARS OLD

At 19 years Galvayne's groove extends all the way down the tooth.

20 to 25 YEARS OLD

The forward slope of the incisors is even more pronounced. Galvayne's groove is disappearing down the tooth.
after 20 years the newly erupted corner incisor has no groove. The groove gradually decreases in length until it disappears at around the age of 30.

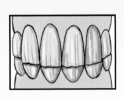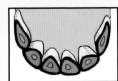

How Many Teeth are there in a Horse's Mouth?

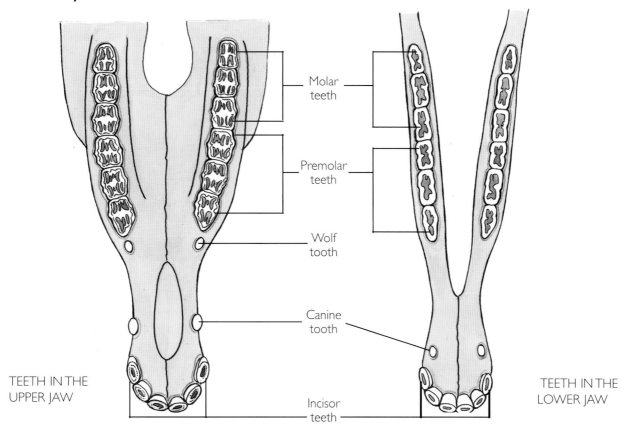

Molar teeth

Premolar teeth

Wolf tooth

Canine tooth

Incisor teeth

TEETH IN THE UPPER JAW

TEETH IN THE LOWER JAW

Milk teeth (also known as deciduous or 'baby' teeth)

TYPE	NUMBER
Incisors	*6 upper and 6 lower.*
Wolf teeth (the 1st premolars)	*(If found!) usually on either side of the upper jaw. Very occasionally found also in the lower jaw.*
Cheek teeth (2nd, 3rd and 4th premolars)	*3 upper and 3 lower (on each side).*

Permanent teeth

TYPE	NUMBER
Incisors	*6 upper and 6 lower.*
Wolf teeth	*(If found) usually on either side of the upper jaw. Very occasionally found in the lower jaw.*
Canine teeth	*Predominantly in male horses, one on each side of the upper and lower jaws.*
Premolars	*3 upper and 3 lower (on each side).*
Molars	*3 upper and 3 lower (on each side).*

Numbering System

Like human teeth, horses' teeth are located by a number, which allows the EDT to specify a certain tooth.

The jaws are divided into four numbered quadrants: the upper right is quadrant 1; the upper left 2; lower left 3 and lower right 4.

The deciduous teeth are also numbered: the upper right 5; upper left 6; lower left 7; lower right 8 (to distinguish them from the permanent teeth).

The permanent teeth are numbered: the incisors (from the middle): 01, 02, 03; the canine 04; the wolf tooth 05; the premolars 06, 07, 08; the molars 09, 10, 11.

Thus, for example, the middle incisor lower left is numbered 301. The 3 signifies the quadrant and the 01 gives the position of the tooth. The 2nd molar upper right will be numbered 110: 1 for the jaw position and 10 for the position of the tooth.

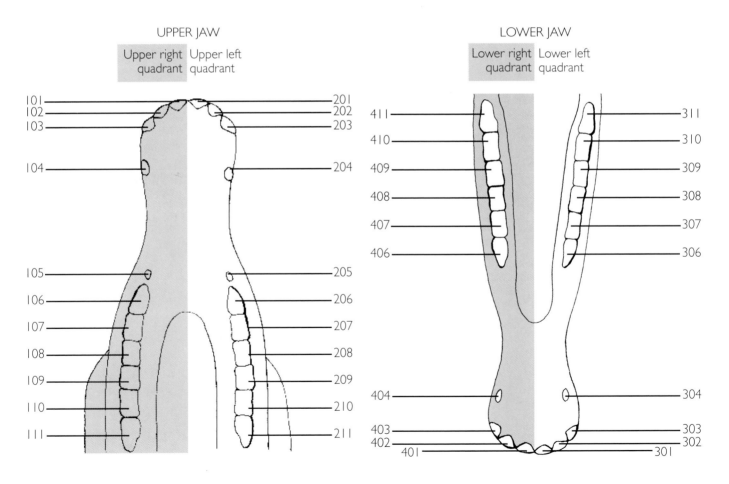

UPPER JAW

| Upper right quadrant | Upper left quadrant |

LOWER JAW

| Lower right quadrant | Lower left quadrant |

Examination of the Teeth and Mouth

As owners we are all responsible for the wellbeing of our horses, and this involves constant observation and evaluation of their health. So many of our horses' problems, both physical and mental, can be linked to pain within the mouth. Many people still believe that their horses will not need their first visit from the EDT before the age of five: after all, he's only young, what possible problems could he have?!

It is necessary to check a horse's mouth and teeth from a very early age, preferably starting as a foal. As not all of us own, or would choose to own, a foal, this cannot always be possible. However, many congenital or hereditary problems present in a new-born foal can be identified, and in some cases corrected if recognised early enough. After the initial examination your horse will need to be checked between the ages of 12 to 18 months. It is important to establish that all the teeth are present, or at least are in the process of erupting. Between the ages of 2 and 5 the horse will shed all 24 milk teeth, to be replaced by between 36 and 40 permanent teeth. Problems are most likely to occur at this age as the permanent teeth erupt; a visit from your EDT every six months during this time is absolutely essential. From the age of six upwards all horses have their permanent teeth: but it is still advisable to continue the six-monthly check-ups.

Older horses will start to run out of tooth—so it is essential to check them regularly. Remember that the teeth are worn away at approximately 2–3mm a year and only have a certain life-span, which will differ from horse to horse depending on how they have been maintained.

Once the teeth get too short and there is no reserve crown left, they will become loose due to a lack of stability in the jaw. Loose teeth will generally cause the horse discomfort and will hinder his abilty to chew food. This leads to the tooth having to be extracted.

Examination by the Owner

It is not recommended that you personally attempt a thorough examination of your horse's mouth and teeth. The horse's jaw has immense crushing power, and by blindly prodding or poking in his mouth you can cause him further pain if a problem exists, and possibly get hurt yourself. However, there are certain signs to look out for and preliminary checks that you can do yourself.

The first and most obvious indicator that your horse may be unwell or suffering with a dental problem is poor condition. This can be a loss of weight brought on by lack of appetite; if your horse is in pain when he eats he will naturally avoid food. The condition of his coat will also be related to his diet. Again, a dull, lack-lustre coat can be the result of a dental problem. However, do not make the mistake of thinking that just because your horse is in good condition he will not have any dental problems. Owners are often shocked to discover how much treatment their seemingly healthy horse may require.

Bad Breath

Stand close to your horse's head and check his breath. The best time to do this is when you are putting on the bridle and he opens his mouth for the bit. Bad breath can be an indication of infection, gum disease or tooth decay. It can also be caused by a build up of fermenting food which has become trapped between 'diastema' (abnormally wide spaces between the teeth). Good oral hygiene is just as important for horses as it is for us.

Discharge from the nose or facial swellings should also raise concern.

Eating Habits

If the mouth is not functioning properly, whether due to an infection of the soft tissue or a dental abnormality, your horse will struggle to eat his food in the normal manner. He may attempt to eat but then drop food or balls of food on the floor. Occasionally a horse may fill his mouth and then move to his water bucket in an attempt to wash the food down. It is helpful to watch him carefully when he is eating, or look in his stable for signs of dropped food. Quite often the water bucket will have food deposits or partially chewed pieces of hay left at the bottom. If the food cannot be chewed effectively it is likely that undigested particles can be found in his droppings. In some extreme cases the horse may stop eating altogether.

Examination by an EDT

If your horse is due for his twice-yearly check-up, or if you are concerned that he may have a problem, your EDT will begin with a thorough examination. This will involve learning about your horse's history, his age, what disciplines he is used for, and past problems or illnesses that he may have suffered from. The examination will not solely be inside the mouth, but will be a complete overall assessment of the head, neck and general appearance.

Symmetry of the face

Initially the examination will involve a close study of the horse's face. The EDT will place his thumbs on either side of the face at the end of the horse's cheekbones and will look at his eyes and ears to check the symmetry of the face. The eyes and the ears should be level. Asymmetry of the skull, where one of the eyes is slightly higher than the other, can affect the horse's vision. An observed object can appear to be in a different place in the field of vision of each eye; in many horses, this may be the cause of frequent spooking. The bone plates of the skull should be flat, with no unevenness. Any deformity in the bones of the jaws may prevent proper development of the teeth within them.

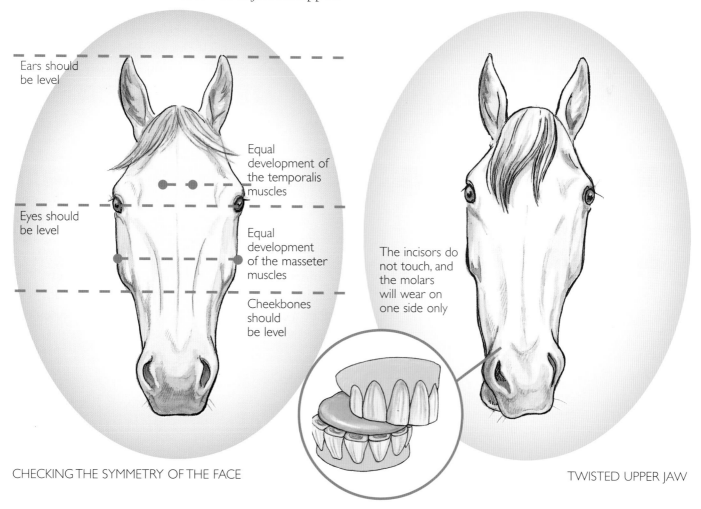

Ears should
be level

Equal
development of
the temporalis
muscles

Eyes should
be level

Equal
development
of the masseter
muscles

Cheekbones
should
be level

The incisors do
not touch, and
the molars
will wear on
one side only

CHECKING THE SYMMETRY OF THE FACE

TWISTED UPPER JAW

27

Dental Cysts

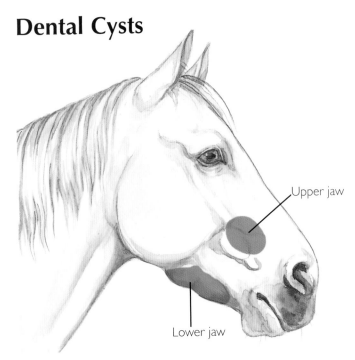

Upper jaw

Lower jaw

POSITION OF DENTAL CYSTS

Starting at the top of the horse's head behind the ears, very light pressure can be applied, working from the poll down, around his eyes and under the jaw. Any lumps, swellings or heat in the skin should be noted, as these can be a result of a dental abnormality, bearing in mind that if the horse is in pain even the slightest of touches can cause a reaction.

Dental cysts are found on the underside of the lower jaw. A young horse sheds his 24 baby teeth between 30 and 48 months old. Approximately 3 to 6 months before this the new permanent teeth begin to grow from the cysts which can be felt externally on the lower jaw. After the baby teeth are shed and the new teeth are in place the cysts will disappear. Dental cysts can also occur in the upper jaw.

Temporalis Muscle

The *temporalis* is the forehead muscle. It begins at the poll, passes down through the hole just above the horse's eye and attaches to the lower jaw. It should lie flat and smooth and have equal development on both sides. A dental problem could cause the horse to chew in an exaggerated upward/downward motion, creating over-development of one or both muscles.

Masseter Muscle

The *masseter muscle* is the broad, flat cheek muscle next to the tongue, and is the largest muscle in the equine head. It is a very important muscle as it elevates the lower jaw and closes the mouth. As with the temporalis muscle, there should be equal development on both sides of the head. If the horse is chewing more on one side of his mouth, the muscle may be more developed on that side.

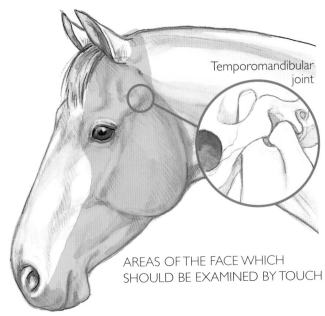

Temporomandibular joint

AREAS OF THE FACE WHICH SHOULD BE EXAMINED BY TOUCH

TMJ

The *temporomandibular joint* is located between the eye and base of the ear. It connects the jaw to the skull. There should be no heat here: during careful manipulation there should be free movement with no clicking sounds or pain.

Teeth

After a careful examination of the horse's skull, it is now time to take a look inside his mouth. Any problems such as swellings or noticeably sore points found during the examination of the head can be a good indicator of problems inside the mouth.

Firstly, the balance of the teeth should be checked. This is done by standing head-on to the horse and gently parting his lips. The biting surface of the incisors should be level; any slants or curves will make it difficult for the horse to maintain the normal side-to-side chewing and grinding action. When the horse's head is down, in the normal grazing position, the front upper and lower incisors, viewed from a side-on position, should be flush with one another. This enables the horse to bite or nip off the grass. By placing a hand under the horse's chin and gently raising his head to an elevated position, the lower jaw should slide backwards. (This is a good experiment to try on yourself. From a standing position look down at the floor and feel the alignment of your teeth and jaw. Now tilt your head back and look up: you will automatically feel your jaw move backwards.)

This is why it is so important to feed horses from the ground, so that the jaw is in alignment. When a horse is fed from a haynet or a manger it puts him at a

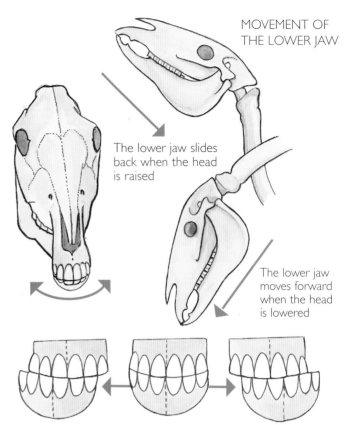

MOVEMENT OF THE LOWER JAW

The lower jaw slides back when the head is raised

The lower jaw moves forward when the head is lowered

The lower jaw should move from side to side

false grazing height, which means that his jaw will have shifted back slightly. This can lead to dental problems and poor drainage from the sinus and nostrils.

Another important test to be carried out by the EDT is to check the sideways, or lateral, movement of the jaw. One hand is placed on the lower jaw with the other across the nose. The lower jaw is then slowly moved from side to side. This should be done in both directions. If met with resistance it is likely that there is uneven wear on the molars and premolars—resulting in sharp and painful hooks.

Lips and Soft Tissue

The lips, tongue and soft tissue of the mouth should be checked for damage. This can be a valuable indicator of the overall condition of the mouth, as many problems which originate in the teeth will eventually go on to affect the cheeks, tongue and gums. Damage can also be caused in many other ways. The lips are a very sensitive area and any ulcers, wounds or injuries can have a huge impact on the horse's feeding habits. This initial examination of the teeth and lips also offers a good opportunity to take note of your horse's breath.

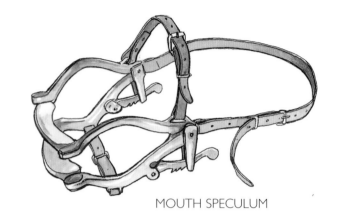

MOUTH SPECULUM

Full Oral Examination

A full oral examination must always involve the use of a *speculum*, or mouth gag, to hold the horse's mouth open and should be performed by an EDT or other qualified person.

At the beginning of the consultation you will be asked about your horse's history—his age, what disciplines he is used for, and any problems or illnesses experienced in the past. Next will come an external assessment of his head and neck. All the checks mentioned in the previous section (symmetry of the bone and muscles, temporomandibular joint, soft tissue etc.) will be carried out, and the general appearance and condition of the horse will be assessed. Then, using the speculum, the mouth will be thoroughly examined from the inside. Any problems will be noted and corrected. When this is not possible (for instance if sedation will be necessary) future treatment will be arranged.

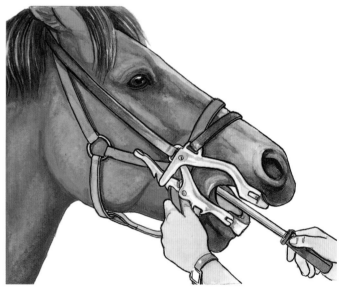

USE OF THE SPECULUM (GAG) AND RASP

Problems of the Teeth and Mouth

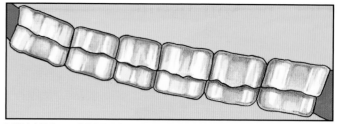

MOLARS — CORRECT APPEARANCE

Hooks and Ramps

Hooks and ramps are caused by uneven wear of the grinding surfaces of the molars. As teeth are constantly erupting, any portion of their surface which is not being worn away will carry on growing—resulting in molars of unequal lengths. The longer teeth will develop either a hook or a ramp effect, which inhibits both the grinding motion of the mouth and the anterior/posterior movement of the lower jaw. This in turn affects the horse's chewing and digestion. Hooks and ramps can cause him when being ridden to open his mouth in an attempt to slide the lower jaw over these longer teeth. They can also cause abnormal force to be exerted on the temporomandibular joint. This is a common problem which can be rectified by grinding off the hooks or ramps—or, ideally, it can be prevented altogether by regular floating (rasping) of the teeth.

Sharp Points

These appear on the outside of the upper cheek teeth and the inside of the lower cheek teeth. They inhibit the lateral excursion of the lower jaw and cause pain. Nearly all horses develop sharp points, but rasping remedies the problem.

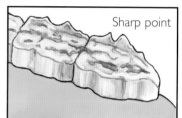

Sharp point

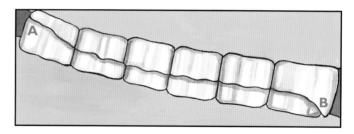

CORRECTION OF RAMP (A) AND HOOK (B) SHOWING THE AREAS OF TEETH WHICH MUST BE REMOVED

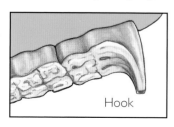

Hook

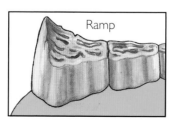

Ramp

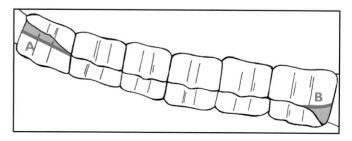

31

Wolf Teeth

The wolf tooth is a very small pointed tooth found in front of the 1st premolar, predominantly on the upper jaw. It has a small root and is best removed. Because of its location in the mouth it can cause great pain and distress for a horse once he is bitted. Occasionally a wolf tooth can remain unseen just below the surface of the gum. It is known as a blind wolf and can be equally as distressing for the horse, since the pressure of the bit lying on the gum over the unerupted tooth can cause pain and discomfort.

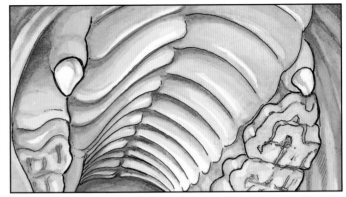

WOLF TEETH (ALSO SHOWING THE RIDGES ON THE ROOF OF THE MOUTH)

Canine Teeth

These are found predominantly in males. An adult horse can have up to 4. Although canine teeth have big, long roots they do not erupt continuously, so do not need treatment—unless and until they start to give trouble. The canines (sometimes referred to as the 'fighting teeth') can become quite sharp and pointed and can cause severe damage to the tongue and cheeks if not dealt with. Filing or grinding down the teeth will relieve this problem. The canines are a common site for accumulations of tartar, which often take the form of balls of brown matter deposited around the tooth. These should be removed to prevent decay of the teeth and gums.

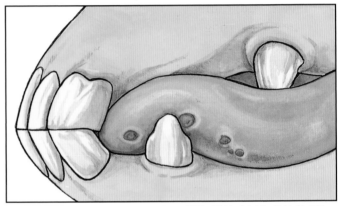

DAMAGE TO THE TONGUE CAUSED BY LONG CANINES

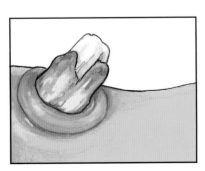

CANINE TOOTH AFFECTED BY TARTAR

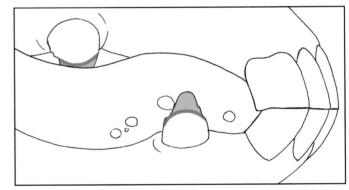

LONG CANINES SHOWING AREAS OF TEETH WHICH MUST BE REMOVED

Surplus and Missing teeth

Occasionally a horse will be found to have supernumary teeth, which can occur in all areas of the mouth—incisors, canines, molars and premolars. A surplus tooth will have no opposing tooth to grind against, and so will keep on erupting until it eventually presses against the gum of the opposite jaw. These long teeth will need regular floating to prevent damage to the gum. Sometimes a tooth can be lost through injury or old age, in which case the tooth directly above or below the resulting gap will not be worn down. It will continue to erupt until it comes into contact with the opposite jaw, causing damage to the gum and pain to the horse. These teeth will also need regular attention throughout the horse's life.

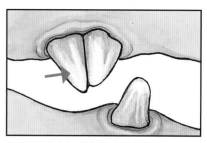

SUPERNUMARY CANINE

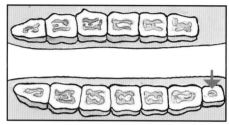

SUPERNUMARY MOLAR

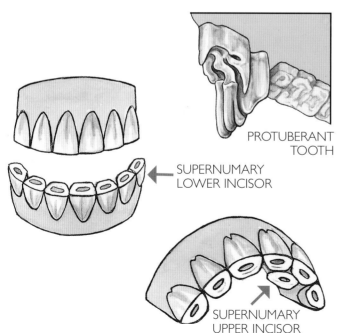

PROTUBERANT TOOTH

SUPERNUMARY LOWER INCISOR

SUPERNUMARY UPPER INCISOR

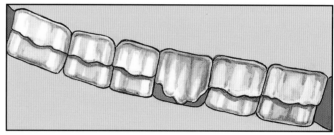

PROTUBERANT TOOTH

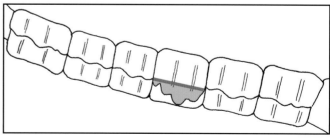

CORRECTION OF PROTUBERANT TOOTH SHOWING THE AREA OF TOOTH WHICH MUST BE REMOVED

Underbite and Overbite

Usually the upper and lower jaws are of equal length—resulting in perfect contact of both incisor and molar teeth. Very occasionally the lower jaw is shorter than the upper jaw; this is known as an 'overbite' or 'parrot mouth'. If the lower jaw is longer than the upper jaw, this is referred to as an 'underbite' or 'sow mouth'. In either case the result will be ongoing dental problems for the horse, as none of the incisor teeth will be in correct contact. All the teeth—incisors, molars and premolars—will need regular rasping to ensure that the horse is able to graze and chew. Fortunately, both the underbite and overbite jaw are rare . It is recommended that horses with either condition should not be used for breeding.

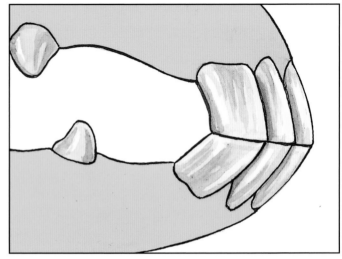

CORRECT ANGLE OF THE INCISORS (SIDE VIEW)

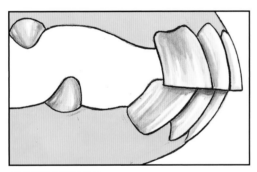

OVERSHOT JAW

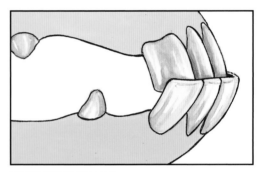

UNDERSHOT JAW

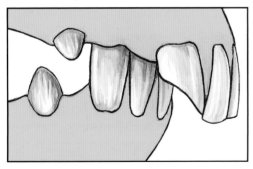

PARROT MOUTH - EXTREME OVERBITE

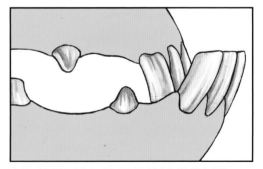

SOW MOUTH - EXTREME UNDERBITE

Step Mouth

There will be a long or protruberant tooth, usually found where an opposing tooth is absent.

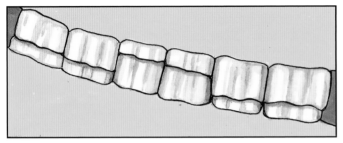

STEP MOUTH

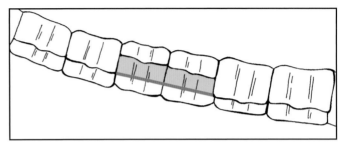

CORRECTION OF STEP MOUTH SHOWING THE AREAS OF TEETH WHICH MUST BE REMOVED

Wave Mouth

When there are protruberant teeth through the whole 'arcade' (an arcade is an individual line of teeth), this is known as a 'wave mouth'. It will affect the anterior/posterior (front to back) movement of the jaw, and inhibit the normal function of the chewing mechanism.

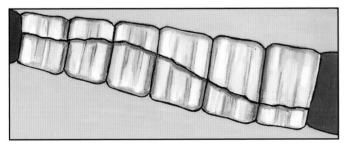

WAVE MOUTH

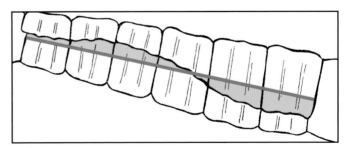

CORRECTION OF WAVE MOUTH SHOWING THE AREAS OF TEETH WHICH MUST BE REMOVED

Retained Deciduous Teeth and Caps

When milk teeth are pushed out by the permanent teeth a thin plate of milk tooth can remain on top of the permanent tooth. This is known as the 'cap'. Caps eventually shed on their own, but when still loose can cause discomfort for the horse. They can also inhibit the eruption of the permanent teeth and therefore require extraction when retained.

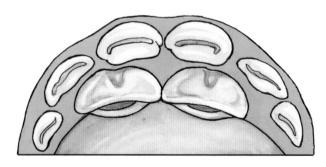

PERMANENT INCISORS IN WRONG PLACE

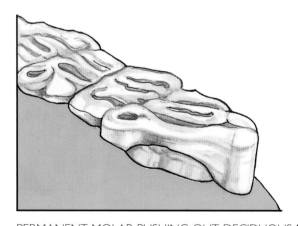

PERMANENT MOLAR PUSHING OUT DECIDUOUS MOLAR

Shear Mouth

The table angles (the angles of the biting surfaces) of the molars become very steep which locks the lower jaw and prevents it from moving laterally (side to side).

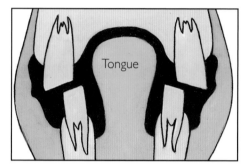

NORMAL MOUTH — CROSS-SECTION OF THE CHEEK
The lower molars are smaller and set closer together than the upper molars. Both sets of molars slope away from the tongue, ideally at an angle of ten to fifteen degrees.

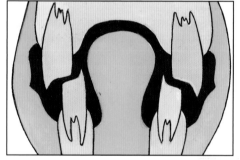

SHARP POINTS
Both sets of molars have developed sharp points through faulty chewing action. These should be removed by rasping.

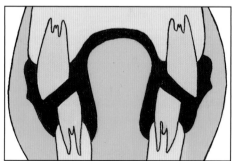

SHEAR MOUTH
The angle of the molars has become too steep.
The correct angle can be reinstated by rasping.

Incisor Problems

There are 3 main incisor problems: *smile*, *frown* and *diagonal*. They all affect the lateral movement of the jaw.

NORMAL APPEARANCE

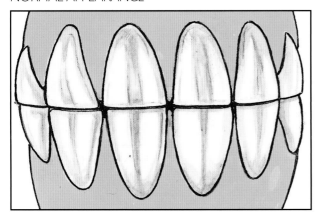

DIAGONAL BITE

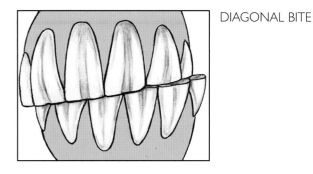

CORRECTION OF DIAGONAL BITE showing the areas of teeth which must be removed

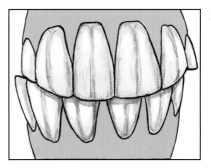

FROWN

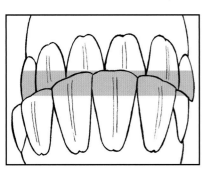

SMILE

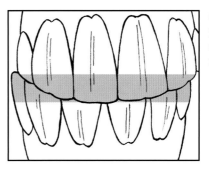

CORRECTION OF FROWN showing the areas of teeth which must be removed

CORRECTION OF SMILE showing the areas of teeth which must be removed

Tooth and Jaw Fractures

Fractures usually occur through injury, such as a kick or a fall onto a hard surface. A crack may not necessarily split the whole tooth; occasionally a piece can break off, which is known as a 'sagittal' or 'slab' fracture. Another type of fracture, known as an 'iotragenic' fracture, is more serious and occurs either across or along the length of the tooth. A tooth which has fractured above the gum-line can be sharp and can inflict damage to the tongue or cheeks. More difficult to detect is the fracture which occurs below the gum-line. This type of fracture can tear the gum, which in turn leads to infection. Other symptoms are bad breath, difficulty in chewing and reaction to extremes of temperature (such as drinking cold water). Jaw fractures can also result from a kick or a severe blow. They occur predominantly in the lower jaw and cause the horse extreme pain. A fracture to the upper jaw is very serious and, again, causes severe pain. This sort of injury can also be the resut of a severe blow to the head or a road traffic accident. Both types of fracture may need specialised surgery in which wire and plates are used to repair the jaw. All fractures will require x-rays to confirm and assess their extent.

Tooth Decay or Cavities

Horses' teeth, as with those of humans, can be affected by decay and cavities. Known as *caries*, the cavities form most commonly in the upper premolars and molars, as these teeth are the most susceptible due to their structure. The upper teeth in horses have what are known as *infundibula*, which are small ponds of cement on their grinding surfaces (see page 17). Infundibula are also present in the front teeth (where they are known as *cups*) and are used in ageing the horse, but they are not as deep as those in the upper premolars and molars. The lower premolars and molars do not have infundibula, and decay is rarely found in them. When the cement inside the infundibula is not developed fully, or the blood supply to it is disrupted—for example when a milk tooth is damaged or removed too early—the cement dies and decays, allowing food and bacteria to enter the inner structure of the tooth and the pulp. This causes inflammation and abscess, usually at the root of the tooth. Thanks to modern advancements in equine dentistry, horses' teeth can now be filled in much the same way as our own, and as long as the cavities are detected early enough during a thorough examination, the teeth can be saved.

SAGITTAL, OR
SLAB FRACTURE

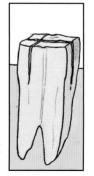

IOTRAGENIC
FRACTURE

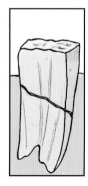

FRACTURE BELOW
THE GUM LINE

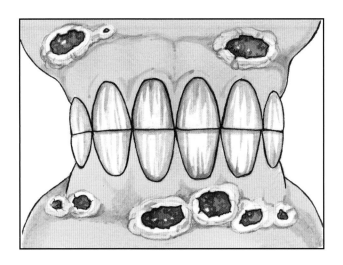

Mouth Ulcers and Sores

Certain sharp or coarse grasses can cause sores and ulcers. Seed pods embedding in the soft tissue of the gums and inside cheeks and lips can lead to inflammation and infection. The seeds can also become trapped between a tooth and the gum. When feeding your horse hay it is always worth doing a quick check for sharp plant material such as thistles, as these can damage the mouth. Irritation from badly-fitting bits can cause sores or ulcers in the mouth.

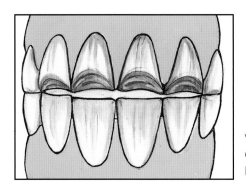

WORN INCISORS CAUSED BY CRIB BITING

Crib Biting

There are many theories as to why horses crib bite—e.g. boredom, dental problems, teething, worm infestation—but none of these theories is definitive. It is also debatable as to whether horses who are stabled next to a crib biter will copy his behaviour and will start cribbing themselves: however, no matter what the cause, the end result of crib biting is always the same—abnormally worn upper front teeth. Horses who bite on a stable door or wooden fence can also suffer from splinters in the mouth. A sore mouth means that the horse is unable to feed properly, which leads to poor condition and performance.

Periodontal Disease

Periodontal disease is a condition causing severe inflammation and destruction of the gums, which can lead to premature tooth loss and even bone destruction. For an animal which can spend up to 20 hours of every day grazing this is a most painful and debilitating disease. It is a very common condition in horses right across the age-spectrum, from as young as two years right into the geriatric years. It starts off as *gingivitis* (inflammation of the *gingiva*, or gum) and at its worst develops into a condition called 'acute ulcerative gingivitis'. In the latter case the inflammation may spread to attack the periodontal ligaments which help to secure the teeth in their sockets. If the ligaments are destroyed, the teeth will become loose and may fall out, or require extraction.

Periodontal disease can be found in all the different equine teeth: the molars and premolars, incisors and the canine teeth of male horses. The most important factor in its treatment and prevention is detection. It can be caused by a number of factors, such as (a) tooth development and eruption problems (all teeth cause inflammation when cutting through the gum, and sometimes infection sets in at this early stage), and (b) the presence of *diastema* (abnormal spaces in between teeth which allow food to become trapped and ferment and decay, causing irritation of the gum around the teeth). Your EDT will be able to recognise this disease and will advise accordingly. Although it has always been present in horses, advanced detection and developments in treatment now mean that this very painful condition can be treated with success.

Tongue and Soft Tissue Damage

The tongue is a mass of muscle attached to the floor of the mouth by soft tissue and the *hyoid bone*. Most tongue injuries occur if horses pull back when tied up by their reins, or by stepping on the reins while in flight. Bits with a severe leverage action in inexperienced hands can also cause damage to the tongue. A bad fall can sometimes, although very rarely, result in the horse biting off the tip of his tongue. More serious damage can occur when the tongue is pulled forcefully out of the side of the mouth as a means of restraint or discipline. Not only can this injure the nerve of the tongue, but it can also fracture the hyoid bone. Although treatment is possible, the injury requires immediate attention, and any repair work must be done under general anaesthetic. The soft tissue or cheeks of the horse are at most risk of damage from sharp teeth. The outer edges of the molars in particular must be kept well rounded to prevent any tearing of the soft tissue.

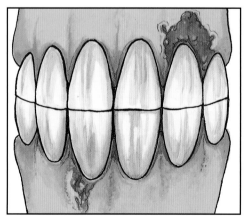

GUM DISEASE

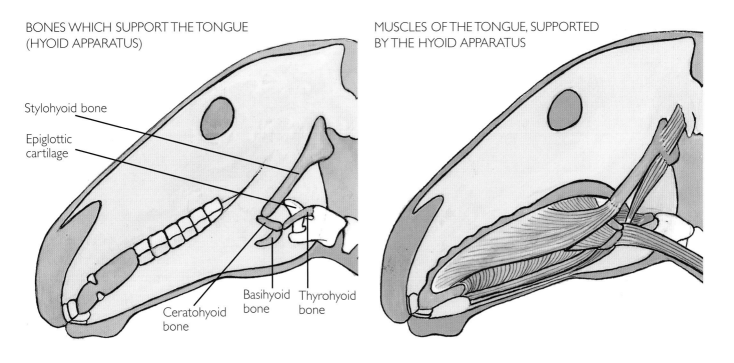

BONES WHICH SUPPORT THE TONGUE
(HYOID APPARATUS)

Stylohyoid bone

Epiglottic
cartilage

Ceratohyoid
bone

Basihyoid
bone

Thyrohyoid
bone

MUSCLES OF THE TONGUE, SUPPORTED
BY THE HYOID APPARATUS

Infection of the Sinuses

The sinuses are large, air-filled cavities. There are two maxillary sinuses, one on each side of the skull, and the frontal sinus, which is located in the middle. The sinuses are linked by a small opening in the bony wall which separates them. The roots of the upper molars project into the maxillary sinus, so any infection in these teeth could easily pass into the deeper structures of the head. Broken teeth, gum disease or a foreign body embedded in a gum socket can all give rise to infection in the sinuses. As this infection can be difficult to eradicate, early diagnosis and treatment are essential.

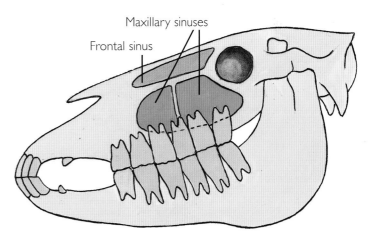

Maxillary sinuses

Frontal sinus

THE LOCATION OF THE SINUSES WITHIN THE SKULL

Injuries to the Lips

These mostly occur when horses are fighting. Sometimes playful nipping from a stable-mate can badly damage the sensitive lips. The use of a twitch applied over-tightly or left on for long periods of time can have devastating consequences: if the blood supply is cut off from the upper lip the flesh can be so severely damaged that it will die, and the lip will lose all function.

Oral Tumours

There are several types of tumours which can be found in the horse's oral cavity; these require veterinary examination and thorough evaluation.

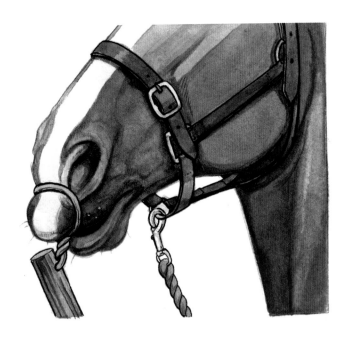

A TWITCH APPLIED TO THE UPPER LIP

Behavioural Problems

Bad behaviour can sometimes be the last resort of a good horse who is in pain: it is his only means of letting his owner know that all is not well. This certainly applies to a horse whose dental health has been badly neglected but who is nevertheless expected to carry a bit in the mouth. Young horses who have never had any dental care may show reluctance to obey commands whilst being ridden; other horses may develop problems over a period of time as the discomfort in the mouth becomes unbearable. On the opposite page are listed some examples of problems which can be linked to pain in the mouth. If your horse is displaying any of them, take note—he may well be trying to tell you something!

Any type of bit, or pressure from the bridle, on a sore and painful mouth can cause unbearable pain. However, rearing and bolting are extreme behavioural problems which should be dealt with by a professional rider or trainer—even though the cause may be severe dental pain.

HEAD HELD
TOO LOW

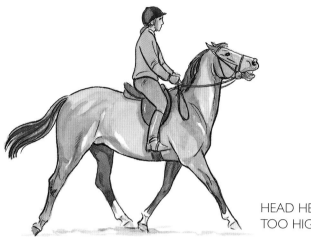

HEAD HELD
TOO HIGH

Problem Behaviour when Being Ridden

- *Difficulties when mounting.*
- *Napping, backing away quickly.*
- *Reluctance to school 'on the bit', or carrying the head unnaturally high or low, or reluctance to accept the fitting of the bridle.*
- *Reluctance to strike off on the correct leg in canter.*
- *Head-shaking.*
- *Rearing.*
- *Bolting.*

Problem Behaviour in Field or Stable

- *Head-shaking or tossing the head up and down.*
- *Difficulties in eating.*
- *Tilting of the head to one side.*

BOLTING

REARING

43

Correct Bitting

Like humans, horses come in all different shapes and sizes—from the miniature Falabella, no bigger than a large dog, to the Shire and Clydesdale, the giants of the horse world. The internal conformation of the horse is just as varied as the external, the mouth and teeth being no exception. Some horses have fat tongues, some thin. The mouth of a Thoroughbred will have finer, more sensitive bars than those of a heavy cob. The roof of the mouth is more concave in some horses than others. The width and size of the lower jaw also differs greatly from one horse to another. Alongside the physical differences, temperament will vary from horse to horse. Some are more sensitive to pain, and degrees of pain, than others. When selecting a bit for your horse, these factors must always be taken into account. The most important point to remember is that all horses are different and must be treated as individuals.

Throughout the horse's life his teeth are consistently changing. It is between the ages of 2 and 5, however, that the greatest changes take place inside the mouth. During this period the horse loses his baby, or milk, teeth and his new, permanent teeth begin to push up through the gum—accompanied, if he is unlucky, by wolf teeth. It is at this time in his life that we choose to introduce a saddle, bridle and rider. Learning to accept all this is hard enough for the horse, but we then add to his problems by putting a bit inside his rather tender mouth. For these reasons we should always give great consideration to a young horse; but we must not forget that an older horse also deserves to be treated with care and to be ridden with gentle hands.

Know your Bits

A vast array of bits—every style, size and sometimes even colour imaginable—is available both at saddleries and online from websites. It is imperative to remember, however, that a bit is not a fashion accessory, and just because it suits your friend's horse it does not mean it will be right for yours.

The purpose of the bit is to enable effective communication between horse and rider. You must select a bit to suit the horse's temperament and age—but also consider the hands that will be at the end of the reins attached to the bit. There are some bits which should only be used by professionals. Severe bits with a strong leverage action should never be used on a horse that is to be ridden by a child or beginner.

Bitting Injuries and their Prevention

Not all problems in the mouth and with the teeth are the result of lack of dental care and maintenance. Some are due to carelessness, or quite simply to poor horsemanship. How many of us have dismounted after a ride or at a show and allowed our horse to casually graze while the reins slip unnoticed over his ears? A horse in this situation could easily take flight and cause terrible injury to his mouth through pulling back or stepping on his reins. Bitting injuries can be very severe, especially to the soft tissue of the mouth and the tongue where there is the possibility of permanent nerve damage. Similar injuries can be caused through a poorly-fitting bridle, a noseband adjusted too tightly or the bit being upside down in the mouth.

Discomfort in the mouth can be caused by the bit becoming trapped between the first upper and the first lower premolars. This not only puts excessive pressure on the tongue, lower bars and gums when the bit is used, but will also force the mouth open. The horse will experience considerable pain, and may react by rearing, running away or running backwards. To prevent this, the outer edges of both upper and lower premolars are rounded off. This is known as a 'bit seat'.

Advice

All saddleries should be capable of offering advice and guidance on bits. There are also specialist shops, particularly online, that deal only in bits. Before changing your horse's bit it is a good idea to consult your EDT, as he/she will be able to advise on what may, or may not, be suitable.

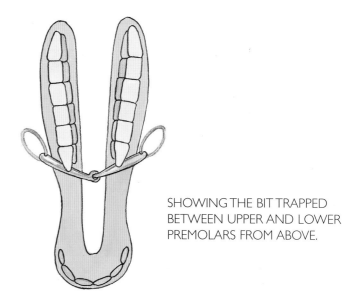

SHOWING THE BIT TRAPPED BETWEEN UPPER AND LOWER PREMOLARS FROM ABOVE.

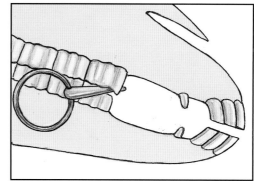

SHOWING THE BIT TRAPPED UNDER THE UPPER PREMOLAR FROM THE SIDE

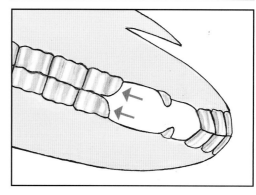

A BIT SEAT WILL PREVENT THIS BY ROUNDING-OFF THE UPPER AND LOWER PREMOLARS

What to Expect from Your EDT

Who do you turn to when you feel it is time for your prized youngster to have his first 'check-up', or your irreplaceable happy hacker needs the sharp edges removing, or your top competition horse is not quite performing as he should?

For some, the answer would be the vet. But when you cannot get hold of your favourite vet or perhaps think you would like to see a specialist 'horse dentist', what are you actually getting? This chapter explains what you can expect from an EDT, from dress and professional etiquette through to the various qualifications that he or she may have, including the training that they have undergone and the full legal and moral boundaries of what they can actually do to your horse.

Qualifications and Training

Firstly, an equine dentist or equine dental technician (EDT as they have to be legally called) is not a vet. He or she will not have attended any of the recognized veterinary colleges or centres of learning to study as a vet. However, this certainly does not mean that the person you are entrusting with your horse's oral welfare woke up one morning and suddenly decided to go out and practise as an EDT.

The study of equine dentistry is a fast-growing profession as more and more people are seeking ways in which to make a successful living within the equestrian world. As popularity in unique fields such as horse psychology, alternative therapies and dentistry grows, the greater is the demand for governing bodies, recognized colleges and qualifications. Unlike the training needed to become a veterinary surgeon, there are many different approaches to learning the necessary skills to become an EDT.

To help unravel all the different letters, abbreviations and qualifications, the following is a brief summary:

EDT   Equine Dental Technician.
MRCVS   Member of the Royal College of Veterinary Surgeons. This is seen after the name of your veterinary surgeon. It tells you that your vet has studied at one of the recognised veterinary colleges. Gaining this qualification involves a minimum of five years' study. Students learn all aspects of animal health including a minimum of 1 year of study of the horse. A veterinary surgeon is the only person fully qualified to administer any drugs that your horse may need for any dental procedures.
BEVA   British Equine Veterinary Association. BEVA was founded in 1961 and is an association for veterinary surgeons who are particularly interested in horses and research into the advancement of equine medicine.
BVDA   British Veterinary Dental Association. An association formed by a group of vets who were interested in veterinary dentistry.
BAEDT   British Association of Equine Dental Technicians. An organization formed in 2001 for veterinary surgeons and qualified equine dental technicians.
WWAED   Worldwide Association of Equine Dentistry. An independent association of EDTs.
IAED   International Association of Equine Dentistry. An association promoting the advancement of equine dentistry.

How To Find an Equine Dentist

Unlimited access to the internet has now made it very easy to locate someone in almost any profession. A simple search will bring up plenty of qualified and experienced EDTs. The earlier information explaining training and the courses that are available and the qualifications gained will help you to select a professional who will look after your horse's teeth. Many will have their own websites while others will advertise in specialist horse magazines or farming and rural publications.

By far the most common or popular means of contact is by word of mouth or recommendation. It is always comforting to know that your EDT comes with a glowing report from your neighbour or your local livery yard.

Choosing the Right EDT for You

Ensuring that your horse has regular, routine dental maintenance is one of the most important things that you can do: his health and happiness rely upon it. The next step is to ensure that you select someone who is right for you and your horse, and can perform his job in a caring, humane and professional manner. As with your farrier, or any other person employed to provide the best care for your horse, selecting on price or availability alone is not always recommended.

To help find the right EDT ensure that he/she:
- *Has the appropriate training and qualifications.*
- *Is friendly, approachable and happy to answer any questions that you may have.*
- *Is willing to supply you with references or put you in touch with current clients or vets with whom they work.*
- *Is keen to discuss and advise on any work your horse may need and to prepare a future treatment plan. Records should be kept.*
- *Turns up to the appointment appropriately dressed, with a full and well-maintained set of instruments.*
- *Has a good manner around your horse. At all times he should be calm and considerate and treat your horse with care.*
- *Has relevant insurance.*
- *Leaves all horses with a dental chart.*

But don't forget that:
- *The work of an EDT is difficult and physically demanding.*
- *You should try to allow a degree of flexibility with time. Appointments can sometimes run over, and treatment cannot always be fitted into a precise time scale.*
- *If you are not happy with something, discuss it with your EDT.*
- *Once work has been carried out on your horse most EDTs will require immediate payment.*
- *A steaming hot cup of tea on a cold morning will always be greatfully received!*

Booking an Appointment and Preparing for the EDT's visit

If this is your first visit from an EDT it would be helpful to give him some basic information about your horse so that he knows what to expect. Don't be afraid to ask questions.

• *Make sure you book a time that is convenient. Allow plenty of time for the visit, as 10 minutes before you dash off to work is not ideal.*
• *Are you comfortable holding your horse whilst the EDT works? If not, get somebody who is.*
• *Ensure that your horse is in his stable before your EDT arrives. Chasing around the field after an uncooperative horse will only increase anxiety on your part and your horse's.*
• *Prepare the stable. It should be clean and well-lit with access to water and electricity if required.*

A horse is a creature of habit, and disrupting his routine could cause unnecessary stress and anxiety. It is therefore worth taking time to plan the appointment with consideration. Will it upset your horse to be left in his stable while others are turned out, or perhaps to be brought in from the field mid-morning when he is used to spending all day out with others? It may be possible for you to arrange for one of his companions to be in a stable nearby for reassurance while the EDT is at work. If you keep your horse in a busy livery yard, try and book your appointment when you know that the yard will be at its quietest.

Communication

It is important for your EDT to know:
• *About your horse and his background.*
• *His age and how long you have owned him.*
• *Any previous health problems that you may be aware of, dental or otherwise.*
• *What activities you take part in with your horse.*
• *If you have experienced any behavioural problems such as rearing, head-shaking or difficulties when putting on his bridle. These could all indicate that your horse has problems inside his mouth.*

Don't be afraid to quiz your EDT. If you are unsure of any procedure that the EDT may recommend, ask him to explain. As this is his 'chosen specialist subject' he will be only too happy to answer any of your questions and put your mind at ease over any concerns.

Finally, remember that this is your horse—your pride and joy—and it is important that he should receive the best treatment possible. Working with your EDT to ensure that all visits are stress and pain free is the priority.

Working with a Veterinary Surgeon

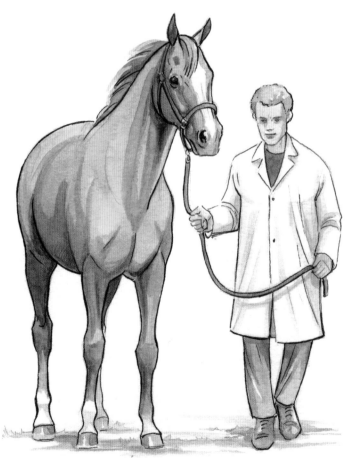

Although the EDT has undergone formal training and spent many months—sometimes years—working alongside professionals in the field to gain knowledge and experience, there are certain aspects of his work where he must call upon the assistance of a qualified veterinarian. The law in Britain is still somewhat unclear on which procedures can be carried out by EDTs and which can only be carried out by veterinary surgeons. Basic routine procedures such as rasping of the teeth, removal of sharp edges and calculus are all within the boundaries of what an EDT can do. However, advanced procedures such as repair of jaw fractures and root canal treatment may only be carried out by a veterinary surgeon.

Although your EDT can examine your horse, carry out certain procedures, identify or diagnose problems and advise treatment, he is unable to prescribe any drugs or administer sedatives. Some of the procedures he can carry out will require the horse to have a sedative with possible follow-up drugs such as anti-inflammatories or antibiotics. It is at this point that your EDT will work alongside your veterinary surgeon.

Instrumentation

Examining a horse's mouth is far more complicated than simply requesting the horse to open his mouth… horses do not always do as they are told! The length of the horse's mouth can be seen by looking at the size of his head—the last molar is a considerable distance away from his lips and incisors. It would be very risky to attempt to examine his teeth without the help of a speculum; to explore the molars right at the back of the mouth would mean inserting your entire arm. If the horse suddenly panicked at this point you would run the risk of a broken arm.

The instruments used to examine and treat the horse's mouth have two functions: firstly to ensure the safety of both horse and human; secondly to perform the necessary work.

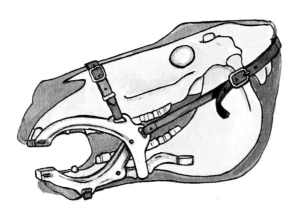

THE SPECULUM CAN BE ADJUSTED TO ALLOW THE MOLARS TO BE EXAMINED

The main items of equipment are:

Headcollar
The headcollar must be adjustable, especially across the nose, so that the mouth can open without restriction.

Headlight / Torch
It is important that your stable is well lit, but even the brightest of lights cannot illuminate the depths of your horse's mouth. A torch or headlight is necessary so that you can examine the mouth and teeth thoroughly.

Drenching Syringe
Water is used to flush out any food inside the horse's mouth before examination. The drenching syringe is also used during and after treatment to remove any debris.

Speculum or Gag
This is the most important tool for the EDT as it allows a thorough and safe examination of the mouth. A leather strap is fitted over the horse's head, similar to that of a headcollar, and the metal part sits inside the mouth. An adjustment on the side of the speculum allows the horse's mouth to be opened and to remain so while any work is carried out. The horse cannot close his mouth until the adjustment is released, ensuring that work can be safely carried out inside the mouth. The speculum can be released at regular intervals during examination and treatment, to ensure that the horse is given a break; it is impossible to do a thorough examination without one.

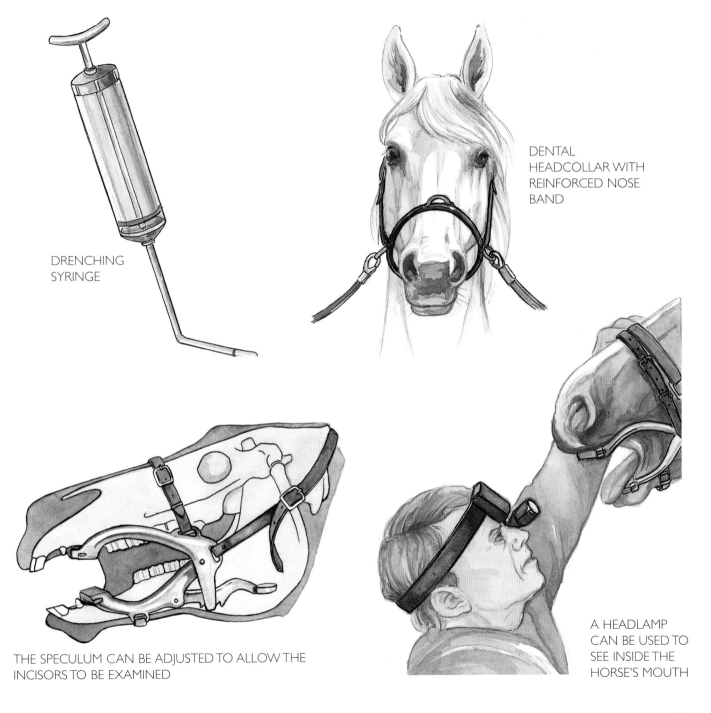

DRENCHING
SYRINGE

DENTAL
HEADCOLLAR WITH
REINFORCED NOSE
BAND

THE SPECULUM CAN BE ADJUSTED TO ALLOW THE
INCISORS TO BE EXAMINED

A HEADLAMP
CAN BE USED TO
SEE INSIDE THE
HORSE'S MOUTH

Hand Floats / Rasps

These are available in many different shapes and sizes. To cope with the tough surface of the tooth, hand floats need to very hard wearing. The blades plane down the teeth to create an even surface.

Forceps

Like floats and rasps, forceps come in a variety of sizes, enabling the EDT to select the right one according to the particular tooth he may be working on. The removal of a molar tooth, for example, requires large extraction forceps, whereas small forceps are used for removing caps or remaining milk teeth.

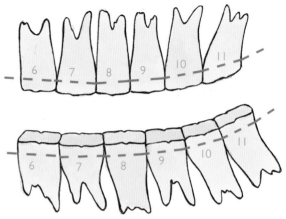

CURVATURE OF THE JAW
The jaw slopes upwards towards the back of the mouth, making the last molars difficult to reach and treat.

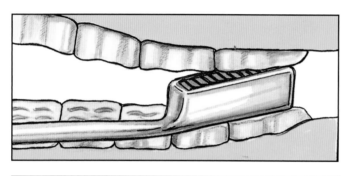

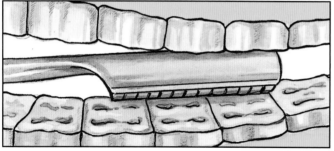

HAND FLOATS (ALSO KNOWN AS RASPS OR FILES). VARIOUS FLOATS CAN BE USED TO SHAPE TEETH IN ALL PARTS OF THE MOUTH.

Elevators and Picks

Dental picks are used to remove food that has become lodged between teeth. They are also useful for elevating the gum tissue prior to extraction of a tooth. The length of the handle on a pick varies, so that work can be carried out on teeth at the back of the mouth.

Power Equipment

Although most sharp edges and overgrowth can be rasped and smoothed down, some are so large that they need to be removed with mechanical grinding instruments. These come in a number of shapes and sizes; as they are very noisy it is recommended that they should be used under sedation.

Bucket

A bucket is used for carrying rasps and for clean water when required. The bucket should preferably be made of stainless steel, as this can easily be cleaned after use.

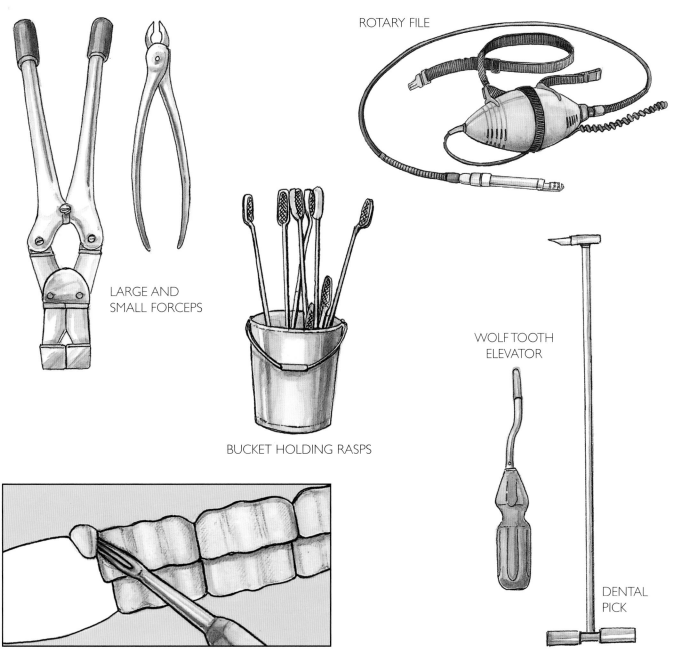

LARGE AND
SMALL FORCEPS

ROTARY FILE

BUCKET HOLDING RASPS

WOLF TOOTH
ELEVATOR

DENTAL
PICK

ELEVATOR — USED TO LOOSEN AND REMOVE WOLF TEETH

Conclusion

There are over 700,000 horses and ponies in the UK today. £4 billion is spent every year, making the British horse industry the second largest economic power in the countryside. Yet in this age of modern science and accessible veterinary treatment, less than half of the horse and pony population regularly receives expert dental care. A much-quoted phrase among farriers is 'No foot, no horse.' How true it could also be for EDTs to say 'No mouth, no horse!'

Equine dentistry is not an alternative form of therapy. It should never be used as a 'one-off' cure for a horse's problem but, as with farriery, should become routine.

This book has not been written with the intention of turning everyone into a dentist or solving all horse problems. Its purpose is partly to give a glimpse at the history and background of this fascinating subject, but more importantly to encourage as many young riders as possible to ensure that their horses are given every ability to perform comfortably in any sphere. Perhaps it may even inspire budding young equestrian enthusiasts to join the steadily increasing number of trained EDTs.

Our world and climate are changing. This may lead to different farming techniques and to the growing of new types of grass forage. In turn, future feeding methods may significantly alter the way we manage and care for our horses. Equine dentistry is constantly evolving. New techniques, progressively modern ideas, and updated instruments make this one of the most exciting fields of work in which to be involved.

Index